Welcome Back, Puffin!

by Dawn Bentley
Illustrated by Beth Stover

SMITHSONIAN INSTITUTION

For Aidan Nicholas Bentley, who wanted me to dedicate the "puppy" book to him. I love you so much!—D.B.

Published by Soundprints, an imprint of Palm Publishing, Norwalk, Connecticut.

Editor: Barbie Heit
Book design: Katie Sears

First Edition 2012
10 9 8 7 6 5 4 3 2 1
Printed in China

Acknowledgements:

Carol LeBlanc, *Vice President*, Smithsonian Enterprises
Brigid Ferraro, *Director of Licensing*, Smithsonian Enterprises

Our special thanks to Ellen Nanney and Kealy Wilson at the Smithsonian Institution's Licensing Division for their help in the creation of this book.
Our very special thanks to Dr. Gary R. Graves, curator of birds of the Department of Vertebrate Zoology at the Smithsonian's National Museum of Natural History for his curatorial review of this title.

Library of Congress Cataloging-in-Publication Data is on file with the Publisher and the Library of Congress

Table of Contents

Puffin is Back!

Far from a cold beach, a **puffin** flies over the ocean to an **island**.

Puffin spends most of her life at sea. Puffin flies to the island once a year to have a baby.

Puffin looks clumsy
when she flies. Her body
is big. Her wings are small.

Puffin tips and wobbles and makes a rough landing. Puffin swims better than she flies!

Puffin finds the same
burrow she uses every year.
The burrow is a long,
dark tunnel.

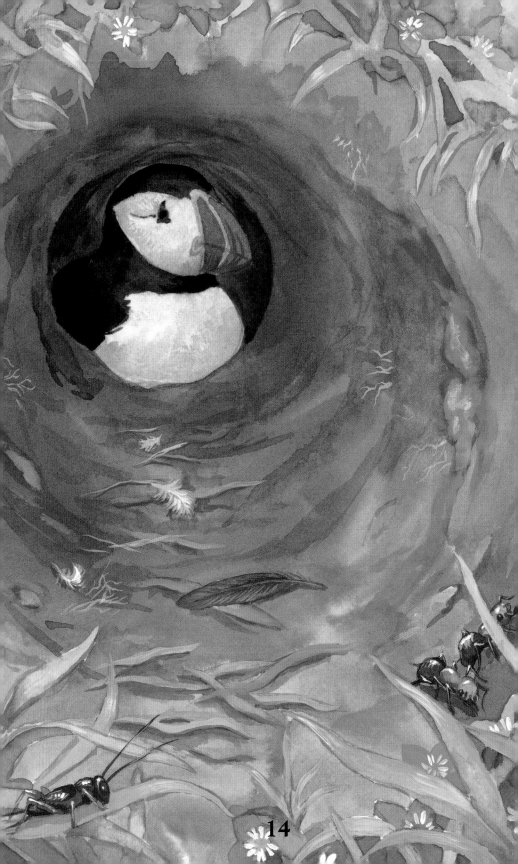

Puffin's Egg

There is a small **nest** at the end of the tunnel. This is where Puffin lays her egg.

Puffin and her **mate** do not sit on their egg like other birds. They tuck the egg close to their bodies. They cover the egg with a wing to keep it warm.

More than a month later,
a baby puffin pecks his way
out of the eggshell.

Baby Puffin is not colorful like his parents. He is covered with fluffy, gray feathers.

Welcome, Baby Puffin

Baby Puffin is hungry!
Feeding the baby is a big job
for Puffin and her mate.

Puffin finds small fish
for Baby Puffin to eat.
Sometimes Baby Puffin
eats ten times a day!

Now, Baby Puffin is almost two months old. He has eaten nearly two thousand fish!

Fly Home, Puffin!

The weather turns cool. Puffin's bright colors begin to fade. The white feathers on her head turn gray. Her bright orange legs turn dark.

It is time for Puffin and her mate to return to sea. It is time for Baby Puffin to be on his own.

33

Puffin jumps off the **cliff**. She flaps her wings. She begins her journey out to sea.

Baby Puffin rests in the burrow. His wing feathers are fully grown. He is ready to leave the island, too.

Baby Puffin runs off the edge of the cliff. He flaps his wings fast. He splashes into the water.

Baby Puffin will need to practice flying. He feels right at home in the water. Other young puffins join him.

Baby Puffin quickly learns how to find fish. Soon he will travel out to sea, just like Puffin.

Glossary

burrow: a hole in which an animal lives or hides

cliff: a high piece of rock, earth or ice

island: land completely surrounded by water

mate: one of a pair of animals that has babies together

nest: a place where eggs are laid and hatched

puffin: a seabird with a short, thick neck and a colorful bill. Puffins live in cold ocean waters.

Wilderness Facts About the Atlantic Puffin

Puffins spend more time in the water than in the air. North Atlantic puffins live in the oceans between Maine, Canada, Greenland, Iceland, Norway, Ireland and Great Britain. Each spring, puffins return to the islands where they were hatched.

Puffins can keep their eyes open
under water. They have clear eyelids
that cover their eyes and protect
them. Puffins also have a special
bill. Ridges on the bill help Puffins
hold fish in place. When they open
their bills to catch another fish, they
don't lose the first one!

In the winter, puffins' beaks are small and not brightly colored. They also lose the bright white feathers on their face. Gray feathers replace them. During this time, they shed their wing feathers and then grow new ones. They cannot fly until the new feathers grow in.

For Additional Learning

Here are some activities to help children better understand the story:

Make Your Own Aquarium

Puffins like to dive into the water and hunt for fish and other sea life. You can make your own aquarium, filled with colorful creatures.

What you will need:

- safety scissors   • glue stick   • a pencil   • markers or crayons
- a few sheets of white construction paper
- 1 sheet of blue construction paper

Directions:

1. Use your pencil to draw small, medium and large fish on white paper. You can also draw sea plants, shells and anything else you'd like to put in your aquarium.

2. Use your markers or crayons to make colorful designs and patterns on your drawings.

3. With the help of an adult, carefully cut out all of your fish, plants and shells.

4. Use your glue stick to place your cut-outs onto the blue construction paper. Now, you have your very own aquarium!

Create a Reading Journal

After your child reads the story, ask him or her to tell you about it using words, pictures or both. He or she can create a reading journal, write about or draw a favorite part of the story, or retell the story in his or her own words. These exercises build reading comprehension skills as well as basic writing skills.